# *Ekphrasis*

## Neil Campbell

NEWTON-LE-WILLOWS

Published in the United Kingdom in 2014
by The Knives Forks And Spoons Press,
122 Birley Street,
Newton-le-Willows,
Merseyside,
WA12 9UN.

ISBN 978-1-909443-41-9



**Acknowledgement:**

The cover image is: *Study of a Woman* by Henri de Toulouse-Lautrec (French, Albi 1864–1901 Saint-André-du-Bois) Publisher: Edouard Kleinmann (French, active 19th century) Date: 1893 Medium: Brush and spatter lithograph printed in olive green on mounted wove paper Credit Line: Alfred Stieglitz Collection, 1949 Accession Number: 49.55.147. www.metmuseum.org

# Table of Contents

# R. B. Kitaj

*Smyrna Greek (Nikos)*

She waits at the bottom of the steps. Her face is blurred by his drunkenness. She is calling out to him through the sheer white flounce of her dress.

He's a handsome young man. Red flares hide the length of his shoes. He's shy, with a mop of thick black hair, and he looks to the ground as the other man comes down the stairs through a light refracted from high windows like a dream.

When the other man passes, hands in pockets, they leave the cherry red light and go up the pale blue stairs. He holds onto the banister until they reach the first door and go inside.

His frustration is flung off like a coat and after she still lies looking at the ceiling. He sleeps with his head on her stomach. He's naked save his shoes and socks. He wakes a few minutes later to the smell of her and he kisses her and licks her until she stops talking. He keeps on kissing and licking, his tongue reaching further inside, his chin resting on her black cushion. Soon she starts to sparkle in the candlelight and he reaches further in, first nose, then head, then neck and shoulders, and in one giant squelch the whole of his body falls in so that his shoes finally come off and drop unnoticed to the floor.

There is a red world of gardenias and he swirls around inside, turning one way then the next like a dolphin through a sea of such flowers. Then he finds a little cloud there, a little pink cloud in among the red, something like the effect of the light on the walls of the stairs but a different colour, tangible, floating, shrunken. Her whole body is rocking so he feels like he's in a skiff on the open sea. He reaches out for the little pink cloud as her body convulses. He cups it in his hands and noses his way through the rollicking red towards the light between her legs, and he pushes his head out first, then his torso, and the rest of his body falls out clumsily because cupped hands can't break a fall. Blinking back into the light he's kicked in the head by her left foot then her right, and the whole blue room is filled with her moaning and she's writhing until his feet finally plop out and she lies there naked and pale. Her head points to the dizzying ceiling that seems to shift and move as though about to be brought down by tremors. Her face is red and her nipples stick out. Sweat drips from her breasts and there's a sparkle of diamonds between her legs.

As she dresses, he sits there naked and shining, feet in sodden socks, hands cupped around the cloud. She goes to the wardrobe of manacles and chains and takes out a chain, wraps it around his wrists so his hands remain securely cupped around the cloud. She takes off his socks and wrings them out, then puts them back on him. She dresses him as best she can, though of course she can't button up his shirt or coat. Finally she puts the shoes back on him.

There's a knock on the door. The door opens and the two men cross each other over the threshold, one man walking down the stairs with his hands cupped around a cloud, the other unzipping his trousers.

# Giovanni Tiepolo

*Madonna of the Goldfinch*

She drinks sweet orange wine in the Plaza De El Salvador and works on a sketch of the church. A fat man comes along. Two children stand behind him. The fat man reaches into the birds, grabs one, breaks its neck and puts it into a sack. He repeats this over and over. The plaza is full of people, eating and drinking and laughing in the shadow of the Church of El Salvador. Nobody says anything to the fat man and he walks off with a sack full of small birds, the two children following.

Paola looks for pictures of the birds on her phone. Shading the screen she sees a painting online of a mother and child, the child holding a goldfinch in his left hand. She turns the page in her sketchpad and starts to copy the picture. Sipping at her sweet orange wine she looks at the many birds in the Plaza De El Salvador, and then starts to sketch them too, trying somehow to capture their movement in strokes of the pencil.

She walks home towards Triana along the Isabel ii Bridge, and sees council workers removing padlocks from the railings. At home she has some flamenquín and then takes out her sketchpad and draws a bridge with padlocks on it, dozens and dozens of them.

# Edward Hopper

*Room in New York*

She presses down on the key. 'How much news can there be?'
'What?'
'How much news can there be?'
'Stop playing that damn note.'
'What note? This note?'
'Funny.'
'No, it isn't'
'What isn't?'
'Funny'
'No, it isn't.'
'This is stupid.'
'Is it?'
'Yes, stupid.'
'I don't....look, leave it.'
'Leave what?'
'Just leave it.'
'Leave what?'
'Just leave it! Leave it! Okay?'
'No need to shout.'
'What?'
'I said there's no need to shout.'

He returns to reading. She remains seated by the piano, playing the same note. He shifts in the red armchair. Her legs shift below the red dress. She stands up and straightens her back, then drifts over to behind the red armchair. She puts his hands on his shoulders and feels them beneath her fingers. She starts to massage. He leans back still reading. As she feels his shoulders they begin to subside. She walks around to the front of the red armchair. He rests the newspaper on his lap and leans back against the red armchair with his eyes closed. She sits down on the newspaper. He puts his right hand between her legs and feels the sheer fabric on either side of his hand. He moves his hand higher, up and under the red of her dress.

He picks the crumpled newspaper off the floor as she goes to the bathroom. He leans forward in the armchair to read, resting the newspaper on the edge of the circular coffee table. She comes back in and sits at the piano. She resumes the same note. She looks down at the key with her knees pointed towards him.

'How was your day?'

'What?'

'How was your day?'

'My day? My day?'

'Yes, *your* day. How was *your* day?'

'Not now. Leave it okay? Not now.'

She plays the same note. He reads the newspaper. The traffic builds below.

# Toulouse Lautrec

*The Kiss*

Among the brothel bedclothes the two women kiss, the woman with the short black hair and the lime green dress on top of the woman with the dark, longer hair wearing a loose white blouse and reaching up from the red bed in response. Red surrounds them on the walls and the bedclothes, the red light of the room. Out of sight, the woman in the lime green dress has her hand between the other woman's legs. There's an ottoman filled with their money at the bottom of the bed. The woman in the lime green half whispers, half kisses the woman below her. In her spasm, the woman in the white shirt grabs the backside of the woman in the lime green, gripping the lime green in both hands. Her body moves in response to the hand inside her. The woman in lime green traces her finger expertly across then plunges fingers. She looks up briefly from the kiss, sees the keyhole of the ottoman and scratch marks around it. She stops kissing a moment and is dragged back down towards the bed. She closes her eyes and resumes kissing. Then she stands up at the end of the bed and slips off her lime green dress. The other woman lies on her back on the red bed and hauls off her white shirt. One woman stands naked by the side of the bed. The other woman lies naked on the bed. The woman standing lowers herself down onto the woman on the bed and they lie down with their breasts pressing together. Each can feel the other's nipples on her breasts. The walls of the red room fall in and crumble across the red bed and hold them together in a red tomb always.

# RB Kitaj

*Los Angeles*

A grey haired man with a grey beard lies in bed, one arm outstretched, his hand between the legs of a red haired woman in a green dress. Behind them is part of a similar picture on the wall. Painted from a different perspective, the woman's hair in the painting on the wall is not the same as the woman's standing. The dresses are slightly different shades of green. And in the painting on the wall the man's hand enters the woman from a different angle. Behind the woman standing there's a pattern of red like lipstick kisses on the wall.

The woman standing has a picture of an angel on her green dress. The man has a similar image on his bedclothes, a different child's face with wings. The man's eyes are closed. He's reaching for this woman among the celluloid dreams of fragmented Los Angeles. The standing woman's left eyebrow is arched, her face strangely emotionless, doll-like. She looks down on his dreams, standing stiffly posed, entirely unaffected by the presence of his hand tilting up rather than down. His head rests on a red pillow. There are red bed sheets with yellow on them. The standing woman's shadow darkens the wall besides the lipstick kisses. Only the painting is real anymore.

When he wakes he does not know that he has the arm wrong. But, she is there on the wall in the empty room. Each night the same dream of a woman in a green dress with a small dark eye and an arched eyebrow. Each day a new canvas in Los Angeles.

# Vincent Van Gogh

*The Langlois Bridge at Arles, 1888*

A sky blue sky with a blending of white clouds. Yellow fields blending with the blue of the lightly rippled river. A shadow across the water below the bridge. On the bridge a black woman with a black umbrella, a distance away, and a distance behind a black figure in a black carriage being pulled by a brown and white horse. On her knees by the water beside the bridge a woman in a red hat looks at her own reflection. Two conifers rise into the sky, one higher than the other. Smoke in the shape of a meringue hangs painted above the white roof of a distant blue building blue as the sky. The yellow fields either side of the river are merged with green and some of that green blends with the yellow on the blue of the river. There's a white building with a red roof to the right. The woman on the bridge looks down the river on the other side of the bridge. Out of sight from this side of the bridge, her son moves away on a shrinking boat. Her husband stops the black carriage and looks towards the brown and white horse, 'What a day eh, boy? What a day.' The man turns in his seat and looks back to his wife. She remains looking at the river. Finally she turns to see her husband looking across at her. She tilts her head down, and then back up, and walks slowly across the bridge, the black umbrella above her head.

# L. S. Lowry

*Man Lying on a Wall*

I worked in the library at the University of Salford. The Clifford Whitworth Library. I never knew Clifford but I would have wished him well. One morning the train was late. So I walked from Oxford Road, Manchester, to Salford instead. It was a nice day. One of those days where you sit in the office and wish you were outside.

When I got to work a little bit late I was told it was the day for Health and Safety training. Now, my old man worked in a warehouse his whole life. All my life I've sat at desks in front of a computer in warm offices surrounded by women. Anyhow I walked into the meeting and there was this little bloke there, probably about fifteen years younger than me. He said, 'You're late,' and I replied, 'I'm early, you're still here.' Now this meant we got off to a bad start. I was only joking at that point. I sat at the table and looked around it and there were about thirty people sitting there in apparent awe of this guy. I'd never seen any of these people before. And this guy at the front, okay, I know it was his job, but I just feel sometimes that people don't have any *perspective*. He delved into his box of tricks and pulled a skeleton out. And I swear to you, this guy, well, he looked like the guy from *The Office*, had the little goatee beard and everything, and when he dragged out this skeleton I almost wet myself. He saw me laughing and I saw in his eyes that he didn't believe what he was doing. I saw the same in the eyes of the people sitting around the table. So what the hell were we all doing there? All of us were just forcing ourselves to believe it because, well, what choice did we have? I could see some guys there, the porters, and I could see that they were just glad of the chance to sit down for a while. The ones with the glint in their eyes like Chris. I used to stand out the back of the library with him and he used to tell me about Sundays. He said he'd just go and watch his lad playing football for a few hours and then come back into work. And he always had these terrible non pc jokes that I won't tell you about here. It was like a generational thing. You had to laugh sometimes, it was the way he told them. But, anyway this guy, what he did then was he unfolded a desk he'd brought with him and he put a stapler on the table next to it. And then he reached over and picked up the stapler. Then he asked us, 'How many times in your working life do you think you would repeat this motion?' And I said, 'Never, I haven't got a stapler.' It was not a great joke and I was never a comedian. I was hoping to get a laugh at that point. But what happened was that I heard this kind of murmur of disapproval. And I was wondering what was wrong with everybody. Where was their sense of humour? Couldn't they see what a waste of time this all was? And you know what came next: the old bend the knees when lifting a box routine. And beard face asked for volunteers, and one of the porters went and did it. Which was fine, that stuff was part of his job. But not the lad from accounts. Or the women from payroll, or the people in personnel. Then the bloke showed us a film with a man sitting at a desk, all hunched over like Marty Feldman in *Young Frankenstein*. And then he stopped the film and asked us to mark each other's posture out of ten. I said I wasn't doing that.

There was something about being sat at that desk that reminded me of being at school. When all the boring kids just sat there and did what they were told, and all the ones with any life in them were always getting into trouble. And it was the same in this health and safety meeting. And this guy (fifteen years younger than me) said that I had come late and had been a negative influence, and that he was going to put this in a report and that I should go back to the office. And when he said that I wondered why I'd even gone to the Health and Safety thing. You see, they do these courses and they make everyone do it. I sit in front of a computer. Chris the porter lifts boxes. Yes, sometimes my back aches from sitting on my arse all day. As I got up to leave someone I'd never seen before muttered, 'grow up' and I turned and asked who it was. This old bald bloke said, 'look we can take this outside if you want.' And I said, 'fine by me.' And this old guy, well, he never moved.

So I started walking home. And it was still sunny. I looked down at the River Irwell as it shone in a crescent below the traffic roaring along the road. There was a heron down there, sat in a tree and looking down at the water. It didn't move at all and I started to think it was plastic. I kept walking down Chapel Street, past the curve of the old trade union building that was in the opening credits for *A Taste of Honey*. Down near Salford Central I went into the Kings Arms and had a pint. And I left there after two pints. Because I'm not a drinker I was already feeling pretty mellow and down near John Dalton Street, where there's that nice bridge that goes over the Irwell, near that pub called the Mark Addy, and not far from the law courts, well I climbed up on that wall and lay down on it. I had the river to my right and the street to my left. Office workers walked past me. I could hear ducks below me in the water. I opened my eyes and saw the sunlight on the water and there were some rowers speeding under the bridge. I thought maybe if I just rolled over and fell into the water that could be something. That could mean something. It would seem that something had actually happened. I went the other way.

There was a formal investigation at work. A disciplinary panel was put together and a meeting arranged for a few weeks later. I was given a big folder full of witness statements and I was asked to write down my own version of events. I was told that I could bring in witnesses of my own. So we had this meeting and I told them that I was having problems at home, and I wrote all that down and a few weeks later I got a formal letter in my pigeonhole. I admit I was nervous. And I opened it and well, I still had a job. In times like this you're lucky to have a job really.

There was this writer Sherwood Anderson that I read about. He said that he owned a paint factory and then one day he just walked out; walked off down the railway tracks and out of town.

# Francisco de Goya

*Perro*

The black car with the spoiler came around the corner and afterwards skidded across to the other side of the road narrowly missing a cyclist. The whimpering dog limped away from the scene and lay under a bush in the shade by an unfinished redevelopment as the black car accelerated away. On the pavement close by a magpie bobbed around.

'Where's Charlie? Mom! Where's Charlie?' asked a little girl called Dani.

'In the garden sweetheart, he's probably in the garden.'

'He's not! I've looked. Mom? Mom!'

'What!'

'He's not in the garden!'

'Alright sweetheart, just wait a minute, I'll come down.' Fastening her robe Kayleigh walked down the stairs and saw her frightened daughter crying. They walked together through the open patio doors and stood looking at the garden with its newly laid squares of lawn and the oblong of wooden fence surrounding.

'Well he's not in the garden.'

'Mum! I told you that.'

'Okay, calm down.'

Near the bush the dog was sleeping and the magpie waited on the telephone wire. Two blonde haired boys came walking down the street and saw the dog sleeping in the shade of the bush. One of the boys poked at the dog with a stick and it whimpered and both boys laughed. They looked around and then dragged the dog through the dust and out from under the bush and started kicking it. The dog tried to bite but was too weak and when it got kicked in the face it lay back down. The two boys grabbed a rear leg each and dragged the dog down the street and around a corner and onto some wasteland behind a revolving billboard. The billboard changed from razor blades to bingo as the boys kicked the dog in the shade. One of the boys took out a screwdriver and stabbed the dog in its already blooded shoulder. The other boy lifted its broken left leg and snapped it, breaking it with his foot so that the bones pointed in two directions and a part of it pierced through the fur and stuck out.

An old woman walked her Jack Russell down the street. Alfie started barking and the woman heard a whimpering below the rattle of the revolving billboard. She stumbled through the undergrowth and on to the patch of wasteland and saw the dog sprawled in the dirt. Alfie was sniffing madly and the woman stood motionless looking at the pathetic image below her. She walked the short distance home and came back to the shade of the billboard with her husband who wrapped the shattered dog in a towel and carried it home with them. They gave the shivering wreck some water and milk and left some food for it and in the morning were surprised to see it still breathing. They called the RSPCA who came round and took the dog away in a van. At the vet's three of the dog's legs were put in casts and it was given all kinds of medications to keep it alive.

A few days later the old woman walked her Jack Russell down the same street and past the revolving billboard but Alfie didn't bark this time. Opposite a cafe she saw a poster attached to a lamppost with a picture of the dog and a phone number underneath.

'Mommy, Mommy, phone!'

'Okay, sweetheart', replied Kayleigh, putting on her dressing gown and coming down the stairs. 'Hello? Oh, hi! Charlie, yes!'

'Mommy?'

'Just a minute sweetheart.'

'Mommy!'

They left the house and got in the car and made the short drive to the dogs' home. The people working there stared hard at Kayleigh and smiled with pity towards Dani. There were a lot of difficult questions to be answered, and much more treatment, before they could take Charlie home. Seeing them again, his bent tail half wagged and he licked Dani on the hand in such a pitiful way that Kayleigh felt like crying.

The two blonde boys sat on a park bench near the revolving billboard, passing a bottle of vodka between them and watching whatever cars came down the road. When it started to get dark and cold they stood up and walked into the middle of the empty road, listening to the sound of the revolving billboard. One of them threw the emptied bottle of vodka as high up into the air as he could and they watched it crash in the road, shattered pieces of clear glass flying everywhere. As it landed they started stumbling and running through the darkness towards the gated estate they called home.

Near another patch of wasteland a dying magpie lay in the dirt with one black and white feather twitching. A group of magpies gathered around, and one of them kept darting in to peck at the dying bird while the others stood around watching.

# RB Kitaj

*A Rush Act*

She truly loves him. He is waiting for someone better to come along. Expert as the redhead is in pleasing him he looks around at the blonde and is already touching her from behind.

Oberon is a ladies' man. He thinks it a triumph to list the women he has fucked, not a tragedy he hasn't found a single woman to love. The giving redhead, Esmie, sucks him in but he'll spit her out along with the others, slave to the seductive power of his own cock.

Oberon likes birds. He walks great distances to see all their varieties in the skies and the trees. When Kandi came along, her long blonde hair blowing and her soft muffin tits ready for touching, he thought he saw in her something of the chough's flying grace. Her hair was perhaps as golden as the sunlit underside of buzzard's wings; her tiny nipples comparable to a robin's beak. Already he's looking away from the monogamous eagle reddened by sunset. Eyebrows like a raven's wings. Left hand poised like a heron. Mouth shaped for repeatable ecstasies in a lifetime he won't know he's lost.

# Francisco De Goya

*Saturn Devouring His Children*

Tom scratches the key around the lock before finally getting it in and turning it the wrong way. Walking into the hallway he hears the TV and goes straight upstairs.

'Bum' comes from the living room as he makes his way back from the bathroom. He closes the door and spreads a newspaper over the carpet beside the bed. Climbing under the covers and lying on his back he looks at the ceiling and then turns onto his side, quickly switching off the lamp.

In the morning there is a trail leading off the side of the bed and down on to the newspaper. He gets up and opens the curtains, squinting out at the street where Colin washes his Sierra. Before dressing he goes to the bathroom to fill the glass with water and then gulps it down. He dresses, and then folds the newspaper and carries it carefully downstairs, going out into the front garden and dropping it into the wheelie bin. The sun dazzles on the windscreen of his Dad's car.

Tom turns on the kettle and it immediately begins to steam. His father is sitting on a deckchair in the back garden, smoking a cigarette and looking at the rows of buddleia. Harry the cat lopes towards the shade and falls onto the grass, four paws spreading in all directions. Tom watches as Harry starts rolling around. When the kettle boils Tom spoons the *Nescafe* into the cup and leaves the steaming cup on the kitchen top while searching in the cupboards. He swallows two tablets and then takes his coffee into the living room where his Mum sits reading the newspaper. There is a cookery programme on the television, and Tom sinks into his seat, the heat from the wall heater seeming to thicken the congestion in his head.

'Did you have a good night?' his Mum asks, smiling.

'Errr...it was okay, yeah.'

'Where did you get to?'

'Ended up in town.'

'What time did you get in?' she asks, although she had heard him stumbling in the bathroom.

'Not that late, really.'

His Dad walks in. 'That's your money gone then.'

'What?'

'That's your money gone for the next two weeks.'

'Not now, Dad.'

'What?'

'I said not now.'

'Free room and board, it's alright for some.'

'Yeah, well.'

'Yeah, well, what?'

'Doesn't matter.'

'Look, just get a job instead of going out all the time. How much did you even have to drink?' he says, shaking his head and going back into the kitchen. 'Do you want a bacon sandwich?' he shouts.

Tom picks up his coffee and goes upstairs without saying anything. He switches on the TV in his room and lies back on the bed watching the cookery programme. A blonde haired woman fondles a carrot in soft focus. Tom crosses his legs and sips the coffee.

After the bacon sandwich Tom waits until his parents are smoking in the living room and then makes himself another coffee, taking it upstairs to his room. He puts on some music, an album by Mike Scott called *Bring 'Em All In*. The sunlight shines across Tom as he lies on the bed. The steam from the coffee spirals in the sun.

*I've tried to do things my own way, and I've tried to do what people say, and I'm going nowhere fast, and I'm turning to you at last. What do you want me to do? What do you want me to do? What do you want me to do Lord?*

Tom falls asleep to the last song on the album, waking at around 4.30. He turns on the TV to watch the match reports coming in. City have been relegated.

Downstairs the family eat their tea in silence until Tom's Mum says, 'We got an email today from Christine.'

'Oh right,' says Tom.

'Do you want to know what she said?' asks Tom's Dad.

'She sent pictures. It looks really beautiful there. She's got her own rock garden. And she's a Buddhist now, isn't that great?' his Mum says, smiling.

'Yeah, that's great, Mum.'

'Buddhist. *Jesus*. What a bloody day.'

After washing up Tom grabs a couple of pieces of bread and takes them up to his room. He lies on his bed and watches *Baywatch*. Lee and Nick are coming at seven. Ten minutes before, Tom takes a checked shirt out of his wardrobe. He walks in the shirt and his underpants to the dining room where he irons the jeans he wore last night. He gets another piece of bread and butters it this time and takes it upstairs. Standing in his sister's old room, he looks through the dark windows at the orange streetlights. He watches until two figures come walking down the street.

Lee and Nick wait for him at the door while he puts on his coat and then closes the door behind him without saying anything.

'Birch?' says Nick.

'Great,' says Tom.

'Come on you sarky bastard,' says Lee.

'Loads out in town tonight, chief,' says Nick.

'You think so?' says Tom.

'Yeah. Saturday is the new Friday.'

'Oh right,' says Tom, smiling.

# R. B. Kitaj

*The Sneeze*

He is naked and sneezing, standing. She is leaning back topless, wearing yellow trousers and at least one red stiletto. Her hair is reminiscent of the 70s. His hair is receding and he's fading away into the background. She looks piqued, her neat breasts and cherry nipples ignored.

When once he would have been feasting on her breasts with his mouth and grappling to remove her yellow trousers with his hands, his illness has left him weak and often incapable. Once such a virile lover, the debilitating illness has reduced his strength. He is more affectionate than ever, cuddling and thoughtful and kind. But her breasts are going cold, the nipples no longer spring to life at his touch. They must get him better. Without this they are only friends. She is at an age where, more than ever, she needs the balm of the afterglow to take the stress from her shoulders and back.

She gets up and covers her breasts, dresses. She goes for his dressing gown, covers his limp body. She goes out into the snow and walks through the village looking for oysters and champagne. When she comes back without them he is sleeping. When he has been sleeping for a few hours, she strips naked and climbs into bed with him. She reaches her hand around to hold his balls. Soon he starts to rise and she strokes the shaft of his cock. Turning him gently onto his back, she fucks him slowly as he sleeps. When he wakes he is no longer sneezing. The illness has raked his body and she grips at his rippled stomach as she rides him. She leans her head away, arching her back, her cherries pointing stiff at the sky. A yellow like her trousers spread across the ceiling and walls, bathing their apartment in the honeymoon colours of Brazil.